Guest Name & Address

Thoughts & Best Wishes

Guest Name & Address

Thoughts & Best Wishes

Guest Name & Address

Thoughts & Best Wishes

Guest Name & Address

Thoughts & Best Wishes

Guest Name & Address

Thoughts & Best Wishes

Guest Name & Address

Thoughts & Best Wishes

Guest Name & Address

Thoughts & Best Wishes

Guest Name & Address

Thoughts & Best Wishes

Guest Name & Address

_____
_____
_____
_____
_____
_____
_____
_____
_____
_____
_____
_____

Thoughts & Best Wishes

Guest Name & Address

Thoughts & Best Wishes

Guest Name & Address

Thoughts & Best Wishes

Guest Name & Address

Thoughts & Best Wishes

Guest Name & Address

Thoughts & Best Wishes

Guest Name & Address

Thoughts & Best Wishes

Guest Name & Address

Thoughts & Best Wishes

Guest Name & Address

Thoughts & Best Wishes

Guest Name & Address

Thoughts & Best Wishes

Guest Name & Address

Thoughts & Best Wishes

Guest Name & Address

_____

_____

_____

_____

_____

_____

_____

_____

_____

_____

Thoughts & Best Wishes

Guest Name & Address

Thoughts & Best Wishes

Guest Name & Address

Thoughts & Best Wishes

Guest Name & Address

Thoughts & Best Wishes

Guest Name & Address

Thoughts & Best Wishes

Guest Name & Address

Thoughts & Best Wishes

Guest Name & Address

Thoughts & Best Wishes

Guest Name & Address

Thoughts & Best Wishes

Guest Name & Address

Thoughts & Best Wishes

Guest Name & Address

Thoughts & Best Wishes

Guest Name & Address

Thoughts & Best Wishes

Guest Name & Address

Thoughts & Best Wishes

Guest Name & Address

Thoughts & Best Wishes

_____
_____
_____
_____
_____
_____
_____
_____
_____
_____
_____
_____
_____

Guest Name & Address

Thoughts & Best Wishes

Guest Name & Address

Thoughts & Best Wishes

_____
_____
_____
_____
_____
_____
_____
_____
_____
_____
_____
_____
_____

Guest Name & Address

Thoughts & Best Wishes

Guest Name & Address

Thoughts & Best Wishes

Guest Name & Address

Thoughts & Best Wishes

Guest Name & Address

Thoughts & Best Wishes

Guest Name & Address

Thoughts & Best Wishes

Guest Name & Address

Thoughts & Best Wishes

Guest Name & Address

Thoughts & Best Wishes

Guest Name & Address

Thoughts & Best Wishes

Guest Name & Address

Thoughts & Best Wishes

Guest Name & Address

_____
_____
_____
_____
_____
_____
_____
_____
_____
_____

Thoughts & Best Wishes

Guest Name & Address

_____
_____
_____
_____
_____
_____
_____
_____
_____
_____
_____

Thoughts & Best Wishes

Guest Name & Address

Thoughts & Best Wishes

Guest Name & Address

Thoughts & Best Wishes

Guest Name & Address

Thoughts & Best Wishes

Guest Name & Address

Thoughts & Best Wishes

Guest Name & Address

Thoughts & Best Wishes

Guest Name & Address

Thoughts & Best Wishes

www.ingramcontent.com/pod-product-compliance
Lightning Source LLC
LaVergne TN
LVHW060210080526
838202LV00052B/4238